CW00665449

ii) E.g. plant B has a different phenotype because it was grown in the shade instead of a sunny area/placed in different environmental conditions to plant A *[1 mark]*.

b) E.g. flower shape/flower colour/leaf shape *[1 mark]* because these are the same in both plants despite the plants growing in different environmental conditions *[1 mark]*.

c) A genetic variant is a different version of a gene *[1 mark]*.

Page 5 — DNA and Protein Synthesis

1 a) Sugar molecule and phosphate group *[1 mark]*

b) 5 *[1 mark]*

3 bases code for 1 amino acid — there are 15 bases shown, so that means the section of DNA could code for 5 amino acids.

2 a)

DNA template

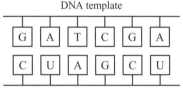

G	A	T	C	G	A
C	U	A	G	C	U

complementary mRNA

[2 marks — 1 mark for correct labelling of C, A and G bases, 1 mark for correct labelling of both U bases.]

b) The mRNA attaches to a ribosome in the cytoplasm *[1 mark]*. The ribosome joins amino acids together in the correct order/following the order of triplets in the mRNA to produce a protein *[1 mark]*.

3 thymine = 24%

The percentage of nucleotides that contain thymine is the same as the percentage that contain adenine because these bases pair up.

100% – 24% – 24% = 52% ÷ 2 = 26%

Cytosine and guanine make up what is left of the sample and there is an equal amount of each.

So guanine = 26% and cytosine = 26%

[3 marks for the correct answer, otherwise 1 mark for thymine = 24% and 1 mark for 100% – 24% – 24%]

Page 6 — Mutations and Genetic Variants

Warm-up

False, True, False

1 a) AAGCTTCCGA *[1 mark]*

b) i) insertion mutation *[1 mark]*

ii) E.g. deletion mutations occur when a base is deleted from the DNA base sequence *[1 mark]*. Substitutions happen when a random base in the sequence is changed to a different base *[1 mark]*.

2 A change in the base sequence of the gene for haemoglobin may change the amino acid sequence which is translated *[1 mark]*. This may mean that the protein produced will be a different shape to the original haemoglobin protein *[1 mark]*. This may affect the ability of the haemoglobin to carry oxygen *[1 mark]*.

Page 7-8 — Genetic Diagrams

Warm-Up

dominant — The allele in a pair that always determines the characteristic shown.

heterozygous — Having two different alleles for a particular gene.

recessive — The allele in a pair that only determines the characteristic shown if two copies of the allele are present.

homozygous — Having two alleles the same for a particular gene.

1 No. The tall allele/T is dominant over the dwarf allele/t, so its presence will determine what characteristic is displayed in the phenotype *[1 mark]*. A tall plant could have the alleles TT or Tt *[1 mark]*.

2 a) E.g.

	n	Nn	Nn
	n	Nn	Nn

[1 mark for the correct genotypes of the offspring]

b) E.g.

	N	n
N	NN	Nn
n	Nn	nn

[1 mark for the correct genotypes of the parents (both Nn), 1 mark for the correct genotypes of the offspring]

ratio of polled calves : horned calves = 3 : 1 *[1 mark]*

You could have drawn a different type of genetic diagram and still got the marks here. Also, don't let the fact that there's one bull and multiple cows throw you — each separate cross between the bull and a cow produces a likely ratio of 3 : 1 polled calves: horned calves, so the overall ratio will still be 3 : 1.

3 a) BB *[1 mark]*, Bb *[1 mark]*

b) i) E.g.

	B	b
b	Bb	bb
b	Bb	bb

[1 mark for the correct genotypes of the parents (Bb and bb), 1 mark for the correct genotypes of the offspring]

probability of offspring being a tabby: 50% / 0.5 / 1 in 2 *[1 mark]*

Again, you could have drawn a different type of genetic diagram and still got the marks here.

ii) 6 × 0.5 = **3**

[1 mark for 3. Allow 1 mark if incorrect answer to part b) i) is used correctly here.]

4 Breed the short-haired hamster with a long-haired hamster *[1 mark]*. If any of the offspring have long hair, then the short-haired hamster must have the genotype Hh *[1 mark]*. If all the offspring have short hair, then the short-haired hamster could have the genotype HH or Hh *[1 mark]*. Further crosses would need to be done to confirm the genotype *[1 mark]*.

Page 9 — More Genetic Diagrams

1 a)

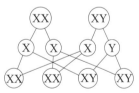

[1 mark]

b) 50 : 50 *[1 mark]*

2 a) i) hh *[1 mark]*

ii) hh *[1 mark]*, Hh *[1 mark]*

b)

	H	h
H	HH	Hh
h	Hh	hh

[1 mark for correct genotypes of parents (both Hh), 1 mark for correct genotypes of offspring.]

probability of having a child who does not have the disorder: 75% *[1 mark]*

Chapter B2

Page 10 — Mendel

1 a) pea plants [1 mark]

b) genes [1 mark]

c) Any two from: e.g. we now know that Mendel's "inherited factors" are genes. / We now know that most characteristics are determined by the interactions of multiple genes (in different parts of the genome). / Scientists are now able to work out the order of nucleotides in a genome/sequence genomes. / Scientists can now use genome sequencing to identify which parts of the genome control different characteristics. / Scientists now have a greater understanding of genetic variants that increase the risk of certain diseases. / Scientists understand how to modify the genome of organisms to introduce specific genes.
[2 marks — 1 mark for each correct answer.]

2 a) 382 ÷ 128 = 2.98,
so ratio of round seeds : wrinkly seeds = **3 : 1** *[1 mark]*

b) E.g. that rounds seeds are dominant over wrinkly seeds. / That round seeds are dominant and wrinkly seeds are recessive. *[1 mark]*

Page 11 — Genome Research and Testing

1) a) personalised medicine *[1 mark]*

b) E.g. it helps doctors to predict how their patient will respond to specific drugs *[1 mark]* and so they will only prescribe drugs that will be most effective for the patient *[1 mark]*.

2 a) E.g. if testing identifies that a person has a genetic variant that increases their risk of developing late onset Alzheimer's *[1 mark]*, they may be able to make diet/lifestyle changes that could reduce their risk of developing the disease *[1 mark]*.

b) E.g. it could cause increased stress for a person if they are identified as having a high risk genetic variant (and they may still never go on to develop Alzheimer's) *[1 mark]*. / A person with a high risk genetic variant may face discrimination from employers *[1 mark]*.

c) i) E.g. testing isn't 100% perfect and could therefore produce a wrong test result, causing unnecessary stress. / Incorrect negative test results could lead to parents who aren't prepared to cope with their child's disorder. / Genetic testing can lead to the destruction of embryos/termination, which some people find unethical. / Some people think that genetic testing could be a 'slippery slope to parents picking the most 'desirable' embryo (e.g. for hair/eye colour) *[1 mark]*.

ii) To determine whether one or both members of the couple are a carrier for a genetic disorder *[1 mark]*.

Page 12-13 — Genetic Engineering

1 a)

6	Selected cells allowed to replicate.
4	Vectors are mixed with and taken up by cells.
1	A useful gene is isolated from an organism's genome.
5	Cells that have taken up vector and useful gene are selected.
2	Copies of the useful gene are made.
3	Each copy is inserted into a vector.

[2 marks for all steps in the correct order, otherwise 1 mark for 4 out of 6 steps in the correct order.]

b) a plasmid *[1 mark]*

2 a) There would be more corn/food for the growing population to eat, as fewer plants would be consumed by pests *[1 mark]*.

b) Any two from: e.g. some people worry that if transplanted genes escape into the environment, they may be picked up by other plants, resulting in superweeds. / Some people worry that GM crops could have a negative impact on food chains/human health. / Some people think that the risks cannot be fully understood without more long-term studies. *[2 marks — 1 mark for each correct answer.]*

3 a) E.g. the eggs could be used to produce insulin for the treatment of diabetes *[1 mark]*. / The eggs could be used to produce antibodies used in therapy for illnesses like arthritis *[1 mark]*.

b) E.g. the hens' health may suffer/embryos may die as a result of the eggs being genetically modified *[1 mark]*. / There may be unforeseen consequences for human health *[1 mark]*.

4 a) E.g. scientists could add the GFP gene to vectors along with the desired gene *[1 mark]*. Cells that took up the vectors containing the desired gene would produce GFP *[1 mark]* and emit green light under UV light, allowing them to be selected by scientists *[1 mark]*.

b) E.g. not all cells will take up the vector containing the desired gene *[1 mark]*. Selection allows scientists to distinguish between cells that have taken up the desired gene and cells that haven't *[1 mark]* so the scientists only replicate cells that contain the desired gene *[1 mark]*.

Chapter B2 — Keeping Healthy

Page 14 — Health and Disease

1 a) pathogens *[1 mark]*

b) A pathogen may have an incubation period after infection of a host, during which there will be no symptoms *[1 mark]*.

2 a) Symptoms are caused because diseases commonly damage host cells *[1 mark]* and impair normal functioning of structures in the organism *[1 mark]*.

b) Communicable, because all the plants in container A have developed the disease *[1 mark]* suggesting it has spread between the plants *[1 mark]*. / Communicable, because it is unlikely that the plants in one container would develop a non-communicable disease and not the other *[1 mark]* when they are all from same batch of seeds and have been grown under the same conditions *[1 mark]*.

c) E.g. the disease that the plants in container A already have protects them from developing the second disease *[1 mark]*.

Remember that some diseases interact with each other, so having one disease can make it more or less likely that an organism will develop other diseases.

Pages 15-16 — How Disease Spreads

Warm-Up

Viruses — These pathogens are not cells. They replicate themselves inside the infected organism's cells.

Protists — These pathogens are eukaryotic and usually single-celled.

Fungi — Some of these pathogens are single-celled, while others have a body made up of hyphae.

Bacteria — These pathogens reproduce rapidly and produce toxins that damage your cells and tissues, making you feel ill.

1 a) fungus *[1 mark]*

b) Through the air (by the wind) *[1 mark]*.

2 a) athlete's foot *[1 mark]*

b) bacteria *[1 mark]*

c) i) crown gall disease *[1 mark]*

ii) Through the soil *[1 mark]*.

3 a) The TMV is spread between plants on surfaces *[1 mark]*, so if she uses the same gloves to handle both the infected and the healthy plants she could spread the disease to the healthy plants *[1 mark]*.

b) E.g. the diameter of the fruit from the infected plants is smaller than the healthy plants *[1 mark]*. The fruit from the infected plants has a lower/smaller mass than the healthy plants *[1 mark]*.

4 a) The virus attacks immune cells/weakens the immune system *[1 mark]*, which makes the body less able to fight off other infections *[1 mark]*.

b) HIV is a sexually transmitted infection/spread via sexual contact *[1 mark]*. Using a condom will reduce the spread of HIV by sexual transmission *[1 mark]*. Malaria is transmitted via animal vectors rather than sexual contact, so using condoms will not affect its transmission *[1 mark]*.

Pages 17-18 — Defending Against Pathogens

1 a) to seal wounds *[1 mark]*

b) It provides a barrier to pathogens *[1 mark]*, preventing them from entering the body *[1 mark]*.

c) The mucus traps pathogens *[1 mark]* and the cilia move the mucus to the back of the throat *[1 mark]*, preventing the pathogens from entering the lungs *[1 mark]*.

2 a) i) Tears contain an enzyme/lysozyme *[1 mark]*, which kills bacteria on the surface of the eye *[1 mark]*.

ii) E.g. hydrochloric acid in the stomach *[1 mark]*. / Chemicals in saliva *[1 mark]*.

b) They make it more difficult for pathogens to survive *[1 mark]* as they out-compete the pathogens for vital resources *[1 mark]*.

3 a) It acts as a barrier to stop pathogens from entering the plant *[1 mark]* and to prevent water from collecting on the leaf, reducing the risk of infection by pathogens that are transferred in water *[1 mark]*.

b) E.g. they have cell walls made of cellulose *[1 mark]*, which act as a physical barrier against pathogens *[1 mark]*.

4 a) There is more rishitin present in all the plants after infection *[1 mark]*, which suggests that the plants produce it in order to defend themselves against the fungal pathogen *[1 mark]*.

b) E.g. the plant may have already been infected with another fungal pathogen *[1 mark]*.

c) E.g. extracted rishitin might be used as a fungicide *[1 mark]*, to prevent damage to food crops by fungal pathogens *[1 mark]*.

Pages 19-20 — The Human Immune System

Warm-up

false, false, true, true

1 Receptors on white blood cells recognise the antigens on the surface of the pathogen *[1 mark]*.

2 a) Some white blood cells can engulf pathogens *[1 mark]*, and the enzymes within the white blood cell then digest the engulfed pathogen, destroying it *[1 mark]*.

b) Antibodies are produced by white blood cells *[1 mark]*. They attach to the antigens on the pathogen *[1 mark]* and disable it *[1 mark]* or target the pathogen for destruction by other white blood cells *[1 mark]*.

3 a) A *[1 mark]*
Memory cells are white blood cells which are produced the first time a person is exposed to a pathogen. They stay in the blood ready to fight off future infections by the same pathogen.

b) At the time of the second exposure the body has some memory cells that will recognise the pathogen's antigens *[1 mark]* and trigger more antibodies to be made *[1 mark]*. This means antibodies are produced much more quickly following the second exposure (so the curve is steeper) *[1 mark]*.

c) The response to the second exposure of the pathogen is so fast that the immune system manages to kill off the pathogen before it has a chance to cause any symptoms *[1 mark]*.

d) White blood cells are specific to only one type of pathogen *[1 mark]*, so the memory cells from the previous infection cannot trigger a rapid response to another pathogen *[1 mark]*. This means the reaction of the immune system is slower and the pathogen has time to cause symptoms of the disease *[1 mark]*.

Page 21 — Reducing and Preventing the Spread of Disease

1 a) Growing a mixture of plants on the same patch of land at the same time *[1 mark]*.

b) E.g. spraying crops with pesticides / fungicides / insecticides *[1 mark]*.

c) Biological control is when another organism is used to control a pest or pathogen *[1 mark]*.

2 How to grade your answer:

Level 0: There is no relevant information. *[No marks]*

Level 1: There is an attempt to discuss the measures which might be taken to limit the spread of hepatitis A and B. The points made are basic and not linked together. *[1 to 2 marks]*

Level 2: There is some discussion of the measures which might be taken to limit the spread of hepatitis A and B. Some of the points made are linked together. *[3 to 4 marks]*

Level 3: There is a full and clear discussion of the measures which might be taken to limit the spread of hepatitis A and B and the potential costs and benefits. The points made are well-linked and the answer has a clear and logical structure. *[5 to 6 marks]*

Here are some points your answer may include:
Individuals may be encouraged to practice simple hygiene methods, such as hand washing, to prevent the spread of hepatitis A. The spread of hepatitis A may also be reduced by improving the sanitation in the town so that people have access to clean drinking water and a good system for disposing of sewage. However, there may be a high initial cost of creating sanitary conditions. Another way to reduce the spread of hepatitis A may be to isolate infected individuals so they are less likely to pass the virus onto others. To prevent the spread of hepatitis B, individuals might be encouraged to use condoms during sexual intercourse. People could be vaccinated against hepatitis A and B so that they are less likely to develop either disease. They would also be less likely to pass the disease on to others, so vaccination would be a benefit to both individuals and to the whole town. However, the vaccination programme is likely to be expensive.

Page 22 — Vaccinations

Warm-Up

inactive, antigens, immune, white, memory

1 a) Because memory cells in the body would be able to immediately produce antibodies to kill off the mumps pathogens *[1 mark]*.

b) The virus was weakened so that it wouldn't cause the disease in the people being vaccinated *[1 mark]*.

c) The large proportion of the population who have been vaccinated against the pathogen won't catch the disease *[1 mark]*. This means that the people who aren't vaccinated are unlikely to catch the disease because there are fewer people able to pass it on *[1 mark]*.

Chapter B2

d) E.g. many diseases may not be serious enough/affect enough people *[1 mark]* to justify spending the large amount of money needed to develop, make and distribute the vaccine *[1 mark]*.

Page 23 — Detecting Diseases

1 a) Examine the colouring of the leaves of the plants *[1 mark]*.

b) E.g. sections of DNA complementary to sections of DNA in a particular pathogen could be added to the sample *[1 mark]*. If the pathogen is present, the DNA strands would bind to the pathogen's DNA and allow it to be identified *[1 mark]*.

2 a) A white blood cell count above the normal range *[1 mark]* may indicate that his immune system is fighting off an infection *[1 mark]*.

During the immune response, white blood cells are cloned (copied) to help fight off the invading pathogens — this means that there will be lots of white blood cells present in the blood when a person has an infection.

b) E.g. they may be able to identify the bacteria present from their appearance *[1 mark]*.

c) So that the samples do not become contaminated *[1 mark]*, as this could lead to the wrong microorganism being detected as the pathogen causing the disease *[1 mark]*.

Pages 24-25 — Culturing Microorganisms

1 a) E.g. the lack of clear zone suggests that antibiotic B had no impact on bacterial growth in culture 2 *[1 mark]*. The bacteria in culture 2 may have been resistant to antibiotic B *[1 mark]*.

b) Antibiotic B is more effective against the bacteria than antibiotic A *[1 mark]*, so there is a larger clear zone around the disc where the bacteria can't grow *[1 mark]*.

c) i) mean = $(85 + 76 + 12 + 80) \div 4$
= $253 \div 4$ = **63** *[2 marks for correct answer, otherwise 1 mark for 85 + 76 + 12 + 80 = 253]*

ii) E.g. the result is an anomaly / not enough antibiotic used / a lower concentration of antibiotic used. *[1 mark]*

2 a) Area = πr^2, radius = 5.0 mm ($\pm$ 0.5 mm)
Area = 3.14×5.0^2 = **78.5 mm²** *[2 marks for correct answer using radius of 5.0 mm ($\pm$ 0.5 mm), otherwise 1 mark for radius = 5.0 mm ($\pm$ 0.5 mm)]*

Make sure you either measure the radius from exactly in the middle of the circle, or that you measure the diameter of the circle and divide it by 2.

b) E.g. sterilise the Petri dish and the agar before using them *[1 mark]*.

c) E.g. pass the inoculating loop through a hot flame before using it *[1 mark]*. Work near a Bunsen flame so that microorganisms are drawn away from the culture *[1 mark]*.

d) The bacteria have not been evenly spread across the agar *[1 mark]*, so it would be very difficult to calculate the size of clear zones around different antibiotics on the plate *[1 mark]*.

Pages 26-27 — Monoclonal Antibodies

Warm-Up

white blood cells, particular, attach to

1 a) identical to each other and bind specifically to one type of antigen. *[1 mark]*

b) produced from lots of clones of a single cell. *[1 mark]*

2 a) So that the animal makes white blood cells which produce antibodies *[1 mark]* that are complementary to the antigen that's been injected *[1 mark]*.

b) Antibody-producing cells (white blood cells) are taken from the animal *[1 mark]*. Those cells which produce the desired antibody are then selected and cultured *[1 mark]*.

3 a) E.g. monoclonal antibodies that bind to the tumour markers on cancer cells *[1 mark]* can be injected into a patient's bloodstream *[1 mark]*. The antibodies will label the cancer cells *[1 mark]* and target them for destruction by the patient's immune system *[1 mark]*. / Monoclonal antibodies that bind to the tumour markers on cancer cells *[1 mark]* can have an anti-cancer drug attached *[1 mark]*, and can be injected into a patient's bloodstream *[1 mark]*. The drug will be targeted directly at the cancer cells *[1 mark]*. *[Maximum of 4 marks available.]*

b) Chemotherapy and radiotherapy can have undesirable side effects *[1 mark]* because they can affect normal body cells as well as cancer cells *[1 mark]*. Monoclonal antibodies allow the specific targeting of cancer cells and so tend to cause less severe side effects than normal chemotherapy or radiotherapy *[1 mark]*.

4 To use the test, the woman should urinate on the patch containing the blue beads *[1 mark]*. If hCG/the hormone is present in the urine, then the monoclonal antibodies on the blue beads will attach to the hormone *[1 mark]*. The urine carries the beads and the hormone to the test strip, where they bind to the antibodies secured on the strip *[1 mark]*. The test strip will then turn blue, showing the hormone is present *[1 mark]*.

You might have learned about how diagnostic sticks work for specific diseases, e.g. malaria. The pregnancy test in this question uses the same idea, the only difference is that the monoclonal antibodies are binding to the hormone in the woman's urine rather than the antigen of a pathogen.

Pages 28-29 — Non-Communicable Diseases

Warm-Up

false, true, false

1 a) It is something that is associated with an increased likelihood of getting a disease *[1 mark]*.

b) E.g. drinking too much alcohol *[1 mark]*.

c) the presence of a particular combination of alleles in a person's genome *[1 mark]*

2 a) There is not enough information about other lifestyle factors that affect the risk of lung cancer *[1 mark]*. It is not known whether either of the women have genetic variants that would make them more susceptible to lung cancer *[1 mark]*.

b) E.g. cardiovascular disease / lung disease/chronic bronchitis *[1 mark]*

3 a) E.g. people in developing countries may find it more difficult to obtain enough protein in their diet compared to people in developed countries *[1 mark]*.

b) Eating too much may lead to obesity *[1 mark]*.
Obesity is a risk factor for type 2 diabetes *[1 mark]*.

4 a) Patient E *[1 mark]*, because their BMI value indicates that they are moderately obese *[1 mark]*.

b) A BMI value can be used to determine whether someone is obese, but obesity is only a risk factor for cardiovascular disease, so it doesn't mean a person will definitely get the disease *[1 mark]*.

c) Any two from: e.g. a lack of exercise *[1 mark]*. / Eating a diet containing too much saturated fat *[1 mark]*. / Smoking *[1 mark]*. / Drinking too much alcohol *[1 mark]*.

Page 30 — Interpreting Data on Disease

1 a) Change = $115.7 - 150.8 = -35.1$
Percentage change = $(-35.1 \div 150.8) \times 100 = $ **−23.3%**
[2 marks for correct answer, otherwise 1 mark for $(-35.1 \div 150.8) \times 100.]

b) Incidence rate of lung cancer in 1994 = 139 per 100 000
So incidence rate per 25 000 = 139 ÷ 4 = **35 males**
[2 marks for correct answer, otherwise 1 mark for incidence rate in 1994 = 139 per 100 000.]

c) They are positively correlated because they both changed in the same direction *[1 mark]*.

d) E.g. the sample only includes males *[1 mark]*, therefore it is not representative of the population of Great Britain as a whole *[1 mark]*.

Page 31 — Investigating Pulse Rate

1 a)

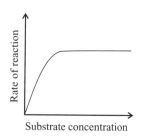

[1 mark for correctly labelled axes, 1 mark for a sensible scale on the y-axis and 1 mark for all bars plotted correctly.]

b) As exercise intensity increased, pulse rate increased *[1 mark]*.

c) She could measure the time taken for her pulse rate to return to her resting pulse rate after each activity *[1 mark]*.

d) Any two from: e.g. the same friend that took Lucy's pulse rate should take her classmate's pulse rate *[1 mark]*. / The classmate should perform the same activities in the same order as Lucy *[1 mark]*. / The classmate should use the same track/surface to perform the activities as Lucy used *[1 mark]*.

Page 32 — Treating Disease

1 a) Antiviral drugs are prescribed to treat the viral infection (by stopping the virus from replicating) *[1 mark]*. Painkillers are prescribed to relieve the pain which results from the infection *[1 mark]*.

b) Any two from: e.g. any potential adverse reactions to the medication in the patient *[1 mark]*. / The cost of the medication *[1 mark]*. / How effective the medication is likely to be in treating the disease in the patient *[1 mark]*. / Whether the patient could get better without the medication *[1 mark]*.

2 a) Minor illnesses are likely to clear up on their own, therefore it isn't necessary to prescribe antibiotics *[1 mark]*. Taking antibiotics will kill non-resistant bacteria in the body *[1 mark]*, giving resistant strains a competitive advantage *[1 mark]* and making them more likely to survive and reproduce *[1 mark]*.

b) Completing the full course of antibiotics will mean that bacteria with some level of resistance are more likely to be killed *[1 mark]*, meaning they can't reproduce and become more common in the population *[1 mark]*.

Page 33 — Treating Cardiovascular Disease

Warm-Up
blood vessels, coronary heart disease, coronary arteries, fatty material, blood flow

1 a) E.g. have a healthy, balanced diet / reduce saturated fat in his diet *[1 mark]*.

b) i) E.g. a stent could be inserted into the artery *[1 mark]* to keep a narrowed artery open and maintain blood flow to the heart *[1 mark]*. / A piece of healthy vessel can be taken from elsewhere *[1 mark]* to bypass the narrowed artery *[1 mark]*.

ii) Any two from: e.g. there is a risk of infection. / There is a risk of bleeding. / There is a risk of developing blood clots. / There is a risk that the surgery might not be successful *[2 marks — 1 mark for each correct answer]*.

c) Any two from: e.g. statins *[1 mark]*. These reduce the rate of fatty deposits forming in blood vessels *[1 mark]*. / Anticoagulants *[1 mark]*. These make blood clots less likely to form *[1 mark]*. / Antihypertensives *[1 mark]*. These reduce blood pressure *[1 mark]*.

Page 34 — Developing New Medicines

1 a) i) cultured human cells and live animals *[1 mark]*
In preclinical trials, animals are used to test the drug on a whole body or multiple body systems, so the animal needs to be alive. You wouldn't want to test on humans at this stage, just in case the drug proves to be dangerous.

ii) effectiveness / safety *[1 mark]*

b) doctor only *[1 mark]*

2 a) He could screen large libraries of chemicals to assess their effectiveness against the target enzyme *[1 mark]*.

b) i) To check that the drug is safe/doesn't have harmful side effects when the body is working normally *[1 mark]*.

ii) E.g. it means they will not be given a potential treatment during the trial *[1 mark]*.

Chapter B3 — Living Together — Food and Ecosystems

Pages 35-36 — Enzymes

1 a) A catalyst increases the rate of a reaction *[1 mark]*.

b) active site *[1 mark]*

c) It means usually only one type of substrate will fit into the active site of a specific enzyme *[1 mark]*.

2 a)

[1 mark]

b) After a certain point, all of the active sites on the enzymes are full *[1 mark]* and increasing substrate concentration does not result in more substrate molecules entering the active sites of enzymes, so the rate of the reaction is not affected *[1 mark]*.

3 At 38 °C Enzyme A will be most active as this is its optimum temperature *[1 mark]*. At 60 °C, enzyme A is denatured and will not be active *[1 mark]* because the shape of the active site has changed and the substrate will no longer 'fit' into the active site *[1 mark]*.

Chapter B3

4 a) i)

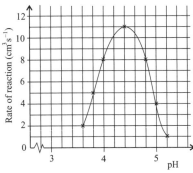

[1 mark for all points correctly plotted, 1 mark for a smooth curve of best fit.]

ii) optimum pH = 4.4 *[1 mark]*

b) The enzyme activity decreases *[1 mark]* because the pH affects the bonds in the enzyme, causing the active site to change shape *[1 mark]* and denaturing the enzyme *[1 mark]*.

Page 37 — More on Enzymes

1 a) 36 °C, as this was the temperature at which the iodine solution stopped turning blue-black first *[1 mark]*, meaning the starch had been broken down the fastest *[1 mark]*.

b) E.g. the amylase was denatured by the high temperature, so the starch was not broken down *[1 mark]*.

c) i) By using a buffer *[1 mark]*.

ii) Any two from: e.g. the concentration of starch solution / the concentration of amylase / the volume of starch and amylase solution added to the iodine / the volume of iodine solution in the wells *[2 marks — 1 mark for each correct answer]*.

d) Test the solutions more frequently (e.g. every 10 seconds) *[1 mark]*.

Pages 38-39 — Photosynthesis

Warm-up

green plants, light, glucose, chlorophyll, chloroplasts

1 a)

	Inputs	Output(s)
First stage of photosynthesis	1. Light 2. Chlorophyll 3. Water	1. Oxygen gas 2. Hydrogen ions
Second stage of photosynthesis	1. Carbon dioxide gas 2. Hydrogen ions	1. Glucose

[5 marks — 1 mark for each correct answer.]

b) Any two from: e.g. it is used during cellular respiration. / It is converted to and stored as starch. / It is used to make larger molecules such as lipids/proteins/carbohydrates. / It is used to make up the organism's biomass. *[2 marks — 1 mark for each correct answer.]*

c) Energy is transferred from the environment during the reaction. *[1 mark]*

2 a) i) Plants produce glucose during photosynthesis and store this glucose as starch *[1 mark]*. If the leaf had been photosynthesising, it would have contained starch and the iodine solution would have turned blue-black *[1 mark]*. If the leaf had not been photosynthesising, it would not have contained starch and would not have turned blue-black *[1 mark]*.

ii) Put the leaf in boiling water to stop any chemical reactions from happening inside the leaf *[1 mark]*. Then put the leaf in a boiling tube with some ethanol and heat it gently in a water bath to remove any chlorophyll *[1 mark]*. Rinse the leaf in cold water and add a few drops of iodine solution to test the leaf for starch *[1 mark]*.

b) Light is needed to transfer energy to the chlorophyll *[1 mark]*. This energy is then used to split water into oxygen gas and hydrogen ions *[1 mark]*.

c) He could perform the starch test on both the green and white parts of the leaf *[1 mark]*. If only the green part of the leaf contains starch and turns blue-black, it shows that chlorophyll is needed for photosynthesis *[1 mark]*.

Page 40 — Investigating the Rate of Photosynthesis

1 a) oxygen *[1 mark]*

b) $1.2 \div 2 = \textbf{0.6 cm}^3\textbf{/h}$ *[1 mark]*

c) i) As the distance from the lamp increases, the rate of gas production decreases *[1 mark]*. This is because the intensity of the light reaching the plant decreases as the flask is placed further away *[1 mark]*, and light intensity is a limiting factor for photosynthesis *[1 mark]*.

ii) E.g. by repeating the experiment with more distances from the light source / at greater distances from the light source *[1 mark]*

d) Different lamps may produce different intensities of light *[1 mark]*, so using the same lamp helps to ensure that the distance between the lamp and the flask is the only thing affecting the light intensity *[1 mark]*.

Page 41-42 — Limiting Factors of Photosynthesis

1 a) inverse square law *[1 mark]*

b) The light intensity reaching the plant would be four times greater *[1 mark]*.

The inverse square law is light intensity ∝ $1/d^2$. This means that as the square of the distance decreases, light intensity increases proportionally — in other words, if you halve the distance, the light intensity will be four times greater.

2 a) The rate of photosynthesis increases between points A and B *[1 mark]*. This is because increasing the temperature (up to the optimum) increases the rate at which the enzymes involved in photosynthesis work *[1 mark]*.

b) Increasing the temperature after point B causes the rate of photosynthesis to fall *[1 mark]*. This is because the temperatures are too high for the enzymes involved in photosynthesis to work *[1 mark]*. At point C, no photosynthesis is occurring because all the enzymes are denatured *[1 mark]*.

3 a) At first, as the carbon dioxide concentration increases, the rate of photosynthesis increases as well *[1 mark]*. Then, at 0.10 arbitrary units of carbon dioxide, the graph flattens out / after 0.10 arbitrary units of carbon dioxide, as the carbon dioxide concentration increases, the rate of photosynthesis no longer increases *[1 mark]*.

b) E.g. increase the temperature *[1 mark]*, increase the light intensity *[1 mark]*.

c)

Rate of photosynthesis (arbitrary units)

Light intensity (arbitrary units)

[1 mark for correctly labelled axes, 1 mark for correctly sketched line.]

Page 43 — Diffusion, Osmosis and Active Transport
Warm-up

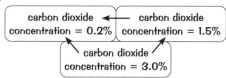

Diffusion is when molecules move down a concentration gradient, from an area with a higher concentration to an area with a lower concentration. So each of the arrows in the diagram should be moving from a cell with a higher concentration of CO_2 to one with a lower concentration of CO_2.

1 a) water *[1 mark]*, partially permeable *[1 mark]*, higher *[1 mark]*, lower *[1 mark]*
  b) A plant is absorbing water from the soil *[1 mark]*.
2 a) ——————————→ *[1 mark]*
  b) ——————————→ *[1 mark]*
  c) ←—————————— *[1 mark]*

For this question you need to work out the relative concentration of the molecules on each side of the membrane and read the question carefully to see what process is involved in their movement.

Page 44 — Transport in Plants and Prokaryotes
1 a) stomata *[1 mark]*
  b) Carbon dioxide diffuses into the leaf *[1 mark]*.
     Water vapour diffuses out of the leaf *[1 mark]*.
     Oxygen diffuses out of the leaf *[1 mark]*.
  c) Gases diffuse from air spaces inside the leaf into the plant cells *[1 mark]* across the cells' partially permeable outer membranes *[1 mark]*.
2 a) To make proteins *[1 mark]*.
  b) The concentration of nitrate ions is higher inside the plant cells than in the soil (outside the plant cells) *[1 mark]*, so the nitrate ions would move out of the plant cells by diffusion *[1 mark]*.
  c) The roots would absorb fewer nitrate ions *[1 mark]* because there would be less ATP to provide the energy needed to actively transport the ions through the cell membrane and into the root *[1 mark]*.

Page 45-46 — Investigating Diffusion and Osmosis
1 a) To allow him to compare the effects of the sucrose concentrations on eggs that didn't have the same initial mass *[1 mark]*.
  b) The water concentration was lower inside the eggs than in the solution in the beaker *[1 mark]*, so the eggs gained mass as water was drawn into them by osmosis *[1 mark]*.
  c)

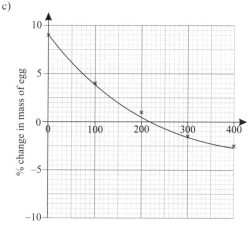

[1 mark for correctly plotting the data, 1 mark for labelling the axes correctly, 1 mark for choosing a sensible scale, 1 mark for drawing a smooth curve of best fit.]

d) 220 mg/cm^3 ($\pm$ 10 mg/cm^3) *[1 mark]*
To work out the concentration of fluid inside the eggs you need to look for the point at which your line of best fit cross the x-axis. This is the point at which there is no change in mass and therefore no movement of water by osmosis — so the concentration of fluid inside the eggs and the sucrose solution must be the same.
2 a) A change in pH *[1 mark]*.
  b) Increasing the concentration of ammonia increases the rate of diffusion *[1 mark]*.
  c) E.g. the volume of the ammonia drops *[1 mark]*, which could have been controlled by measuring them with a dropping pipette *[1 mark]*. / The size of the litmus paper *[1 mark]* which could have been controlled by measuring the length and width of the strip with a ruler *[1 mark]*. / The distance the ammonia had to travel *[1 mark]*, which could have been controlled by making sure the distance between the cotton wool and litmus paper was the same each time *[1 mark]*.
  d) i) E.g. estimating the point at which the litmus paper has changed colour *[1 mark]*.
     ii) E.g. by repeating the experiment and calculating a mean *[1 mark]*.

Page 47 — Xylem and Phloem
Warm-up
transpiration, evaporation, leaves, transpiration stream, roots, translocation, sugars
1 a) i) phloem *[1 mark]*
     ii) To transport food substances (mainly sugars) up and down the stem from photosynthetic to non-photosynthetic tissues/to growing and storage tissues *[1 mark]*. / To enable translocation *[1 mark]*.
  b) i) The xylem have thick, stiff cellulose walls strengthened by lignin *[1 mark]* which give the plant support *[1 mark]*.
     ii) E.g. the xylem vessels carry water that is being drawn up the stem (from the roots to the leaves) as a result of transpiration *[1 mark]*.

Page 48 — Stomata
1 a) X: stomata *[1 mark]*
     Y: guard cells *[1 mark]*
  b) They are responsible for opening and closing stomata *[1 mark]*, in order to control gas exchange and water loss from a leaf *[1 mark]*.
  c) Paint thin layers of clear nail varnish onto a leaf *[1 mark]*. Place clear sticky tape onto the painted leaf and use it to peel the varnish off. The varnish will have an impression of the leaf's surface *[1 mark]*. Stick the tape onto a microscope slide for viewing *[1 mark]*.
2 a) Leaf A = (25.2 + 20.1 + 18.7 + 17.9) ÷ 4 = **20.5 μm** (3 s.f.) *[1 mark]*
     Leaf B = (14.7 + 12.8 + 14.1 + 13.2) ÷ 4 = **13.7 μm** (3 s.f.) *[1 mark]*
  b) Leaf B *[1 mark]* because stomata begin to close when light intensity decreases / stomata open more as light intensity increases *[1 mark]*. This means the leaf with the lower mean stomatal diameter (leaf B) will have had the measurements taken in conditions of lower light intensity *[1 mark]*.

Page 49 — Transpiration Rate
1 a) (0.92 − 1.35) ÷ 1.35 x 100 = **31.9%** *[2 marks for the correct answer or 1 mark for correct working]*
  b) i) As air flow increases, loss of mass increases *[1 mark]*.
     ii) Air flow causes water vapour around the leaf to be swept away, creating a lower concentration of water outside the leaf *[1 mark]*. This causes water to diffuse out of the leaf faster (from an area of higher concentration to an area of lower concentration), so the plant loses mass *[1 mark]*.

c)   E.g. they could place a shoot next in a darkened room/ cupboard and one next to a lamp *[1 mark]*. / They could place shoots next to lamps that emit different light intensities *[1 mark]*.

Page 50 — Using a Potometer

1 a)

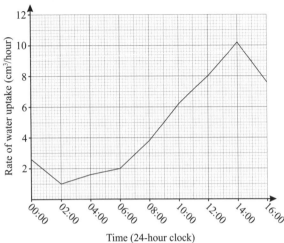

Time (24-hour clock)

[1 mark for using a sensible scale for the y-axis, 1 mark for labelling the y-axis, 1 mark for accurately plotting the points, 1 mark for connecting the points with straight lines through the centre of each point.]

It might sound a bit obvious, but make sure you always use a sharp pencil to draw graphs like this. Your graph might turn out inaccurate if your pencil is blunt, which could lose you marks.

b)   5.0 cm³/hour *[1 mark]*
c)   5.1 cm³/hour *[1 mark]*
d)   Any two from: e.g. light intensity increased. / Temperature increased. / Air flow around the leaf improved. / Humidity decreased *[2 marks — 1 mark for each correct answer]*.

Pages 51-52 — Ecosystems and Interactions Between Organisms

Warm-Up
A — Moisture level, pH of soil, Temperature, Light intensity, Toxic chemicals
B — Number of predators, Food availability, Number of competitors, Presence of pathogens
1   All the organisms of different species living in a habitat. *[1 mark]*
2 a) Bioaccumulation *[1 mark]*
  b) It means that the concentration of DDT will have increased at each stage of the food chain *[1 mark]*.
3 a) E.g. the population of prickly acacia may have increased *[1 mark]* because they grow best when there is plenty of water *[1 mark]*.
  b) E.g. the prickly acacia may become distributed over a wider area *[1 mark]* as they may spread into areas that were previously too cold for them *[1 mark]*.
  c) E.g. the prickly acacia may compete with the grasses for resources (such as light, water, space and nutrients) causing their populations to decrease *[1 mark]*.
4 a) E.g. the populations of roe deer may have increased because their natural predators are extinct / because there was lots of available resources that were not already being exploited *[1 mark]*. Bigger populations of roe deer may have led to increased competition between the roe deer for resources, e.g. food, shelter *[1 mark]*, so they may have had to expand their habitat in search of more resources *[1 mark]*.
  b) The population of roe deer would probably decrease *[1 mark]* because the lynx will prey on the roe deer *[1 mark]*.

Pages 53-54 — Investigating Ecosystems

1 a) i)   To make sure the sample is representative of the whole area *[1 mark]*.
     ii) E.g. divide the field into a grid and place the quadrats at coordinates selected using a random number generator *[1 mark]*.
  b)   13 buttercups *[1 mark]*
The mode/modal number is the most frequently occurring number.
  c)   15.5 buttercups *[1 mark]*
To answer this question, simply put the numbers of buttercups in each quadrat in order from the smallest to the largest, like this: 12, 13, 13, 13, 15, 16, 16, 23, 23, 26. The median number is halfway along this list — so it lies halfway between 15 and 16.
  d)   15 + 13 + 16 + 23 + 26 + 23 + 13 + 12 + 16 + 13 = 170
           170 ÷ 10 = 17 buttercups per 0.5 m² *[1 mark]*
  e)   17 × 2 = 34 per m²
           34 × 1750 = 59 500 buttercups
           [2 marks for the correct answer, otherwise 1 mark for multiplying answer to part d) by 2.]
2 a)   (85 × 94) ÷ 6 = 1331.66... = **1332 worms** *[1 mark]*
  b)   A brightly coloured tag might affect the worms' chances of survival by making them more visible to predators (e.g birds) *[1 mark]*. This would reduce the worms' population size and so give an inaccurate estimate *[1 mark]*.
  c)   So that the population of worms had time to move about / redistribute before the second sampling *[1 mark]*.
  d)   E.g. capture the worms over a longer period of time to get a bigger sample. / Repeat the investigation several times and calculate the mean *[1 mark]*.
  e)   E.g. that no worms died/were born between the first and second samples. / That marking hasn't affected the worms' chance of survival *[1 mark]*.

Pages 55-56 — More on Investigating Ecosystems

1 a) i)   Spots and stripes *[1 mark]*
     ii) Butterfly F *[1 mark]*
  b)   Any two from: e.g. a key with more butterflies included *[1 mark]*. / A key with higher quality photographs *[1 mark]*. / A key with colour photographs *[1 mark]*. / A key with more features listed *[1 mark]*.
2 a)   Zones B and C *[1 mark]*
  b)   long grass *[1 mark]*
  c)   Zone A is closest to the pond where the soil has more moisture *[1 mark]*. Zone A also has a higher light intensity *[1 mark]*.
  d)   Zone B *[1 mark]* because only short grass grows in zone B *[1 mark]*.
  e)   E.g. a quadrat could be placed at regular intervals along the transect *[1 mark]* and samples taken by estimating the percentage cover of the four different plant types *[1 mark]*.

Page 57 — Investigating Factors Affecting Distribution

1 a)   E.g. the distribution of organisms is affected by abiotic factors such as pH *[1 mark]*. By recording soil pH at the different quadrat sites, the students can see if there is any evidence that pH is affecting the distribution of the plant species in the area *[1 mark]*.
  b) i)   E.g. soil moisture level / light intensity *[1 mark]*.
     ii)   E.g. soil moisture meter / light sensor *[1 mark]*.
2 a)   one *[1 mark]*
  b)   The further away from the road, the greater the number of lichen species *[1 mark]* because the concentration of sulfur dioxide from cars gets lower further from the road *[1 mark]*.
  c)   25 m *[1 mark]*

Chapter B3

Page 58 — Food Chains and Food Webs

1   Row C *[1 mark]*

Remember, producers (the algae in this example) are eaten by primary consumers (the krill) and primary consumers are eaten by secondary consumers (the seals).

2 a)   E.g. capybaras are eaten by jaguars. / Biomass is transferred from the capybaras to the jaguars *[1 mark]*.

Don't get mixed up about the direction of the arrows in food webs and food chains. The arrows show the direction of biomass transfer. So the organism the arrow is pointing from is eaten by the organism the arrow is pointing to, i.e. the capybara is eaten by the jaguar.

     b) i)   E.g. the population of bats may decrease because there will be less food for them to eat *[1 mark]*.

        ii)   E.g. the population of mice may increase because they are not being preyed on by as many bats. / The population of mice may decrease because the bats need more food *[1 mark]*.

     c)   Any two from: flowering tree/banana tree/grass *[2 marks — 1 mark for each correct answer]*.

Page 59 — Pyramids of Biomass and Number

Warm-Up

D

There are four trophic levels described in the question and the base should be the widest part of the pyramid for the food chain described, since the producers have the largest biomass.

1 a)   organisms / living material *[1 mark]*, shrubs *[1 mark]*, bottom *[1 mark]*, four *[1 mark]*, lions *[1 mark]*, biomass/energy *[1 mark]*

   b)   Shrubs ⟶ Impalas ⟶ Lions ⟶ Fleas *[1 mark]*

   c)   E.g. the number of fleas is likely to be higher than the number of lions *[1 mark]*, so the top bar would be longer in the pyramid of numbers *[1 mark]*.

Page 60 — Biomass Transfer

1 a)   Some biomass is lost when organisms respire *[1 mark]*. Parts of the organisms at each trophic level don't get eaten (e.g. willow tree roots/hedgehog bones/hedgehog spines) *[1 mark]*. Some biomass is egested at each trophic level *[1 mark]*.

   b) $3.4 \div 37 \times 100 = $ **9.2% *[1 mark]***

   c)   So much biomass is lost at each stage that there's not enough left to support organisms at a fifth trophic level *[1 mark]*.

2 a)   Because the animals are kept warm and don't move around much, they respire less *[1 mark]*. This means less biomass is lost from the food chain/more biomass is transferred from the animals to humans *[1 mark]*.

   b)   E.g. eat some of the parts of animals that don't usually get eaten *[1 mark]*.

For example, parts such as the kidneys, liver and heart are eaten a lot less than prime cuts of meat. If these parts were always eaten too, it would improve the efficiency of biomass transfer from animals to humans.

Page 61 — Making and Breaking Biological Molecules

1   By eating both producers and other consumers *[1 mark]*.

2 a)   A: simple sugars (e.g. glucose) *[1 mark]*
        B: amino acids *[1 mark]*
        C: lipid *[1 mark]*
        D: glycerol *[1 mark]*

   b)   Consumers need to be able to break down large molecules into smaller components so that they can be absorbed into the bloodstream and transported to cells *[1 mark]* where they can be built up into larger molecules and used to form the biomass of the consumer *[1 mark]*.

Page 62 — Testing for Biological Molecules

Warm-up

Biuret test — Proteins
Benedict's test — Reducing sugars
Emulsion test — Lipids
Iodine test — Starch

1 a)   E.g. add the sample of egg whites to a test tube containing ethanol *[1 mark]*. Shake the tube for about a minute until the egg whites dissolve *[1 mark]*. Pour the solution into water *[1 mark]*. If a milky emulsion forms, then there are lipids present; if not, then no lipids are present *[1 mark]*.

   b)   E.g. add some biuret reagent/a few drops of sodium hydroxide and some copper(II) sulfate solution to a sample of the egg whites *[1 mark]*. If proteins are present, then the solution will turn purple *[1 mark]* and if not then the solution will be blue *[1 mark]*.

2 a)   He should add Benedict's reagent to each of the solutions *[1 mark]*, then heat the test tubes in a water bath that's set to 75 °C *[1 mark]*. He should then look out for the formation of a coloured precipitate and note the colour if one is formed *[1 mark]*.

Glucose is a reducing sugar so the Benedict's test can be used to determine the relative concentrations of glucose in the test tubes.

   b)

	Tube 1	Tube 2	Tube 3	Tube 4
substance observed	yellow precipitate	blue solution	red precipitate	green precipitate
glucose concentration (M)	0.1	0	1	0.02

[1 mark]

The higher the concentration of glucose in the solution, the further the colour change goes along the following scale: blue — green — yellow — orange — brick red. If no precipitate forms then there are no reducing sugars in the solution.

Page 63 — Cycles in Ecosystems

1 a)   E.g. air/soil/fossil fuels/waste *[1 mark]*

Abiotic just means 'not living' so you can choose anything from the diagram that isn't alive.

   b)   respiration *[1 mark]*

   c)   photosynthesis *[1 mark]*

   d)   They release carbon dioxide when they are burned *[1 mark]*.

   e)   Animal waste and dead plants and animals are being broken down by decomposers/microorganisms *[1 mark]*. These decomposers/microorganisms release carbon dioxide back into the air by respiration as they break down the material *[1 mark]*.

2   The trees have fewer leaves so less photosynthesis will take place *[1 mark]*. This means that less carbon dioxide will be removed from the air, contributing to a greater concentration of carbon dioxide in the atmosphere in winter *[1 mark]*.

Page 64 — More on Cycles in Ecosystems

Warm-up

evaporate, water vapour, cools, precipitation, runoff

1 a)   A — evaporation *[1 mark]*
        B — precipitation *[1 mark]*
        C — condensation *[1 mark]*

   b) i)   When an organism or cell gets rid of the waste products of chemical reactions *[1 mark]*.

       ii)   Excretion, e.g. sweating/urination/breathing out *[1 mark]* is how animals return water to the environment *[1 mark]*.

   c)   Through transpiration *[1 mark]* and in their tissues via food chains *[1 mark]*.

Chapter B4

Page 65-66 — Decomposition

Warm-up

true, false, false, true, false

1 a) $12 \div 10 = 1.2$ units of mould/day *[1 mark]*

b)   Mould contains enzymes which digest the tomatoes and bread *[1 mark]*. The rate of enzyme-controlled reactions increases with temperature (up to a point) *[1 mark]*, so it's likely that the rate of decomposition was fastest near the radiator as it will have been warmest there *[1 mark]*.

c)   Most decomposers need water to survive *[1 mark]*. Biscuits are drier than the other types of food, so the mould wasn't able to grow on them in this time period *[1 mark]*.

2 a)   How to grade your answer:

Level 0:   There is no relevant information. *[No marks]*

Level 1:   There is an attempt to explain how methane is produced by landfill sites or how using it to generate electricity could be beneficial to the environment. The points made are basic and not linked together. *[1 to 2 marks]*

Level 2:   There is some explanation of how methane is produced by landfill sites and how using it to generate electricity could be beneficial to the environment. Some of the points made are linked together. *[3 to 4 marks]*

Level 3:   There is a full and clear explanation of how methane is produced by landfill sites and how using it to generate electricity could be beneficial to the environment. The points made are well-linked and the answer has a clear and logical structure *[5 to 6 marks]*

Here are some points your answer may include:

Landfill sites are low in oxygen, so the decomposers there tend to respire anaerobically.

Anaerobically respiring decomposers produce methane, which is a greenhouse gas. Carbon dioxide is also a greenhouse gas, although methane has a much greater greenhouse effect.

Increasing levels of greenhouse gases are causing the average global temperature to rise. This is global warming.

Burning methane to generate electricity will reduce the amount of methane released into the atmosphere and so reduce the contribution of landfill sites to global warming.

Burning methane instead of burning fossil fuels will also reduce the amount of carbon dioxide released into the atmosphere.

b)   A properly managed compost heap will have lots of oxygen available *[1 mark]* meaning decomposers will respire aerobically *[1 mark]* and produce carbon dioxide instead of methane *[1 mark]*.

Chapter B4 — Using Food and Controlling Growth

Page 67-68 — Respiration

1 a)   It is an exothermic reaction that transfers energy from the breakdown of glucose *[1 mark]*.

b)   oxygen *[1 mark]*

2 a) $5.88 \div 20 = \textbf{0.29 cm}^3\textbf{/min}$ (2 s.f.) *[1 mark]*

b)   Glucose *[1 mark]* because this substrate produced the most CO_2 / the rate of respiration was fastest for this substrate *[1 mark]*.

The more CO_2 produced, the more O_2 is needed to produce it. And a faster rate of respiration means that more O_2 is used up in the same time period.

c)   Any two from: e.g. the volume of substrate solution / the concentration of substrate solution / the temperature of the water bath / the amount of yeast added to each test tube *[2 marks — 1 mark for each correct answer]*.

d)   the mitochondria *[1 mark]*

3 a)   E.g. the snail must have enough oxygen for two hours / the snail must not dry out *[1 mark]*.

b)   The glass beads are acting as a control in the experiment *[1 mark]* to show that any change in the carbon dioxide concentration of Beaker A is due to the snail and not some other factor *[1 mark]*.

c) i)   The percentage of carbon dioxide in the air has increased over the two hours because the snail releases carbon dioxide as it respires *[1 mark]*.

ii)   It would have decreased *[1 mark]* because the snail would have used up oxygen as it respired *[1 mark]*.

d)   The internal temperature of Beaker A would be higher than that of Beaker B / the internal temperature of Beaker A would increase whereas the internal temperature of Beaker B would stay the same *[1 mark]* because during respiration energy is transferred to the environment by heat *[1 mark]*.

Page 69-70 — More on Respiration

1 a) i)   E.g. glucose *[1 mark]*

ii)   oxygen *[1 mark]*

b)   Aerobic respiration has a higher ATP yield/is more efficient than anaerobic respiration *[1 mark]*.

c)   In plants the products of anaerobic respiration are ethanol *[1 mark]* and carbon dioxide *[1 mark]*, whereas in animals the only product is lactic acid *[1 mark]*.

2 a)   anaerobic respiration *[1 mark]*

b)   glucose $\rightarrow$ ethanol + carbon dioxide

[2 marks, 1 mark for each side of the equation correct]

c)   E.g. if the container wasn't sealed tightly, oxygen would be able to enter the container *[1 mark]*. This could lead to the yeast respiring aerobically, meaning that ethanol/alcohol wouldn't be produced *[1 mark]*.

3   The root cells of the rice plant will be respiring anaerobically, since the roots are submerged in water (where there is little/ no oxygen) *[1 mark]*. One of the products of anaerobic respiration in plants is ethanol *[1 mark]*. Therefore it is advantageous for the roots of the rice plants to have a higher tolerance to ethanol to prevent them being poisoned by the ethanol they produce *[1 mark]*.

4 a)   Oxygen consumption increased rapidly at first then increased more slowly *[1 mark]*, until around 8 minutes when it levelled off *[1 mark]*.

b)   In the final two minutes of exercise, the man's oxygen consumption remained constant *[1 mark]*. This suggests that his muscles were respiring anaerobically (as well as aerobically) to supply the extra energy needed for his muscles to continue to work harder, as this process doesn't require oxygen *[1 mark]*.

Page 71 — The Cell Cycle and Mitosis

1 a)   The number of subcellular structures is increasing *[1 mark]*. The DNA is duplicating *[1 mark]*.

b)   The cytoplasm is dividing *[1 mark]*. The cell membrane is dividing *[1 mark]*.

c)   They are genetically identical *[1 mark]*.

d)   So the organism can grow *[1 mark]*.

e) i)   A change (mutation) in one of the genes that controls cell division *[1 mark]*.

ii)   Uncontrolled cell division can result in a mass of abnormal cells called a tumour *[1 mark]*. Tumours that invade and destroy surrounding tissue are called cancers *[1 mark]*.

Chapter B4

Page 72 — Microscopy

1 a) Cell A is half as wide as Cell B *[1 mark]*.
  b) Cell A has 0.5^2 of the area of Cell B. / Cell A has a quarter of the area of Cell B *[1 mark]*.
2 a) Electron microscopes have a higher magnification *[1 mark]* and a higher resolution than light microscopes *[1 mark]*.
  b) E.g. smaller structures can be seen under an electron microscope / structures can be seen with greater detail *[1 mark]*. This has allowed scientists to develop explanations for how the internal structures of, e.g. mitochondria/chloroplasts, relate to their functions *[1 mark]*.
3 a) Staining the chromosomes allows them to be seen more clearly *[1 mark]*.
  b) A *[1 mark]* because the chromosomes in cell A are spread out/not condensed *[1 mark]*.

Pages 73-74 — More Microscopy

Warm-up
1

	÷ 1000 will convert to:	× 1000 will convert to:	in standard form, original unit will be:
mm	m	μm	$\times 10^{-3}$ m
μm	**mm**	**nm**	$\times 10^{-6}$ m
nm	**μm**	**pm**	$\times 10^{-9}$ m
pm	**nm**		$\times 10^{-12}$ m

2 Total magnification = **eyepiece lens** magnification × **objective lens** magnification

It doesn't matter which way round you write eyepiece lens and objective lens in the formula.

$$\text{magnification} = \frac{\text{measured size}}{\textbf{actual size}}$$

1 a) i) Total magnification = eyepiece lens magnification × objective lens magnification
        Total magnification = 10 × 100 = **× 1000** *[1 mark]*
   ii) 25 μm *[1 mark]*

The height of the cells is about 2 and a half times the length of the scale bar.

  b) 8×10^{-6} m *[1 mark]*
2 a) length of cell A in image = 24 mm
       magnification = measured size ÷ actual size
                     = 24 ÷ 0.012 = **× 2000**
       [2 marks for correct answer, otherwise 1 mark for length of cell = 24 mm.]
  b) measured size = magnification × actual size
       400 × 0.012 = **4.8 mm** *[2 marks for correct answer, otherwise 1 mark for 400 × 0.012.]*
3 a) actual size = measured size ÷ magnification
       actual size = 10 mm ÷ 1000 = 0.01 mm
       0.01 mm x 1000 = **10 μm** *[3 marks for correct answer, otherwise 1 mark for 10 ÷ 1000, 1 mark for 0.01 × 1000.]*
  b) 4×10^{-5} = 0.00004 mm
       0.00004 mm × 1000 = 0.04 μm
       0.04 μm × 1000 = **40 nm** *[3 marks for correct answer, otherwise 1 mark for 0.00004 × 1000, 1 mark for 0.04 × 1000.]*

Page 75 — Sexual Reproduction and Meiosis

1 a) Gametes contain half the number of chromosomes in other body cells. *[1 mark]*
  b) Four genetically different daughter cells. *[1 mark]*
  c) zygote *[1 mark]*

2 a)

[1 mark]

The left-hand diagram in the question shows a cell containing two pairs of chromosomes just before it undergoes meiosis. The first division causes these pairs to split up so that the two new cells only contain one chromosome from each pair. In the second division the chromosome in each cell is pulled apart so that each of the four gametes end up containing only one chromosome arm.

  b) It's needed to produce cells/gametes with half the number of chromosomes in the body cells *[1 mark]* so that when two gametes fuse at fertilisation, chromosomes from the mother and father can pair up *[1 mark]* and the zygote ends up with the full number of chromosomes *[1 mark]*.

Page 76 — Stem Cells

Warm-up
differentiate, specialised, early human embryos, growing, any cell type
1 a) i) E.g. embryonic stem cells have the potential to produce any type of cell at all *[1 mark]*, whereas adult stem cells are less versatile *[1 mark]*.
   ii) E.g. some people think it's wrong to destroy a potential human life *[1 mark]*.
  b) meristem tissue *[1 mark]*

For this question it's no good writing 'the tips of roots' or 'the tips of shoots' — you've been asked to name the tissue that produces stem cells, not give its location within a plant.

2 a) Switch on the genes that produce insulin/the genes that produce proteins required by an insulin-secreting cell *[1 mark]*. Switch off any genes which produce proteins that aren't required *[1 mark]*.
  b) E.g. there may be a risk of tumour development *[1 mark]* if the rate at which the new insulin-secreting cells divide inside the patient can't be controlled *[1 mark]*. / There may be a risk of disease transmission from the donor to the recipient *[1 mark]* if viruses are present within the embryonic stem cells used to develop the new insulin-secreting cells *[1 mark]*.

Page 77-78 — Plant Growth

Warm-up
false, true, false, true
1 a) To stimulate the cutting to produce roots *[1 mark]*.
  b) auxins *[1 mark]*
2 a) The seedlings in Set A have grown straight up but the seedlings in Set B have grown sideways (towards the light) *[1 mark]*.
  b) It allows the plant to receive maximum light for photosynthesis *[1 mark]*.
  c) Auxins moved towards the shaded side of the shoot/away from the light side of the shoot *[1 mark]*. The auxins made the cells elongate/grow faster on the shaded side *[1 mark]* so the shoot bent towards the light *[1 mark]*.
3 a) the root *[1 mark]*
  b) In roots, auxins inhibit cell elongation *[1 mark]*. In a sideways growing root, more auxin will be present on the lower side of the growing tip *[1 mark]*, causing the cells on the top to elongate faster and the root to grow downwards *[1 mark]*.

c)   E.g. it makes the root more likely to anchor itself in the soil / find water and minerals in the soil *[1 mark]*.

Page 79 — More on Plant Growth

1 a)   seed germination *[1 mark]*
  b)   Ethene stimulates cells that connect the leaf to the rest of the plant to expand *[1 mark]*. This breaks their cell walls and causes the leaves to fall off the plant *[1 mark]*.
  c)   It stimulates enzymes that cause fruit to ripen *[1 mark]*.
  d)   E.g. gibberellins can be used to alter the dormancy of seeds and make them germinate at times of the year that they wouldn't normally/make all the seeds in a batch germinate at the same time *[1 mark]*. / Gibberellins can be used to trigger 'bolting' in plants that makes them flower earlier than usual/ under conditions in which they wouldn't usually flower *[1 mark]*.

2 a)   Placing the agar block on one side of the shoot caused an uneven distribution of auxins/meant auxins were only present on one side of the shoot *[1 mark]*. This caused the shoot to only elongate on the side with the agar block on it *[1 mark]* so the shoot bends away from the side with the block *[1 mark]*.
  b)   E.g. lack of light would prevent auxin from redistributing to the shaded side of the shoot *[1 mark]*.

Chapter B5 — The Human Body — Staying Alive

Page 80 — Exchange of Materials

1 a)   As a multicellular organism, the stickleback has a relatively small surface area to volume ratio *[1 mark]*. This means diffusion to and from cells deep within its body is too slow *[1 mark]*. To speed up the exchange of substances, it needs specialised exchange surfaces to increase its surface area to volume ratio *[1 mark]* and a mass transport system to move substances around its body (so substances have a shorter distance to diffuse) *[1 mark]*.
  b)   These organisms would have a relatively large surface area to volume ratio *[1 mark]* so oxygen would be able to diffuse across the outer surface quickly enough to supply all the body cells *[1 mark]*.

2 a)   X = $(3 \times 3) \times 6 = $ **54 cm²** *[1 mark]*
      Y = $3 \times 3 \times 3 = $ **27 cm³** *[1 mark]*
      Z = $150 \div 125 = $ **1.2** *[1 mark]*
  b) $5 \times 5 \times 5$, because it has the smallest surface area to volume ratio *[1 mark]*.

As this cube had the smallest surface area in relation to its volume, it would take the acid longest to diffuse throughout this cube and change its colour.

Page 81 — Human Exchange Surfaces

1 a)   C *[1 mark]*
  b)   Out of the blood *[1 mark]*.
2   Any two from: e.g. the small intestine is covered in villi *[1 mark]*. This increases the surface area for absorption *[1 mark]*. / The small intestine has a good blood supply *[1 mark]*. This allows absorption to happen quickly *[1 mark]*. / The villi have a single layer of surface cells *[1 mark]*. This means that substances only have a short distance to diffuse across, so absorption can happen quickly *[1 mark]*. / The cells of the villi have partially permeable membranes *[1 mark]*. These regulate the movement of substances across them *[1 mark]*.

3   The breakdown of the walls of the alveoli means that the surface area in the lungs is reduced *[1 mark]*. This reduces the amount of gas exchange that can take place in the lungs *[1 mark]* and therefore the amount of oxygen that can diffuse into the blood *[1 mark]*.

Page 82-83 — The Circulatory System

Warm-up

	vena cava	pulmonary vein	pulmonary artery	aorta
oxygenated		✓		✓
deoxygenated	✓		✓	

1 a)   X = aorta *[1 mark]*
      Y = pulmonary vein *[1 mark]*
      Z = (right) ventricle *[1 mark]*
  b)   3, 5, 2, 4, 1 *[2 marks for all correct, 1 mark if all but one are in sequence.]*

2 a)   The wall of the left ventricle is thicker than the wall of the right ventricle *[1 mark]*. This is because the left ventricle needs to generate greater pressure than the right ventricle *[1 mark]* because it pumps blood around the whole body, whereas the right ventricle only pumps blood to the lungs *[1 mark]*.
  b)   When the ventricles contract, the valves to the atria close and the valves to the blood vessels open *[1 mark]*. This prevents backflow/the blood from flowing backwards and makes sure that blood flows in the right direction (out of the heart) *[1 mark]*.

3 a)   Mitochondria provide the muscle cells with ATP *[1 mark]* which transfers the energy needed for the cardiac muscle to contract and pump blood around the body *[1 mark]*.
  b) i) coronary arteries *[1 mark]*
     ii) E.g. if one of these arteries became blocked, less glucose and oxygen would be able to reach the cells of the heart *[1 mark]* and they would die *[1 mark]*.

Page 84 — Blood Vessels

1 a) i) A *[1 mark]*
     ii) Arteries carry blood under high pressure (unlike veins or capillaries) *[1 mark]*. This means they need thick muscular walls for strength *[1 mark]* and the walls of blood vessel A are the thickest compared to its lumen *[1 mark]*.
  b) i) veins *[1 mark]*
     ii) Blood in veins is at a low pressure *[1 mark]* so the valves help to keep the blood flowing in the right direction/prevent backflow *[1 mark]*.
  c)   Capillaries carry blood close to cells to exchange substances with them *[1 mark]*. Having walls that are only one cell thick increases the rate at which substances can diffuse across them *[1 mark]*, by decreasing the distance over which diffusion occurs *[1 mark]*.

Page 85 — Blood

1 a)   plasma *[1 mark]*
  b)   Any three from: e.g. carbon dioxide / urea / hormones / water / glucose / amino acids / antibodies *[1 mark for each correct answer. Maximum of 3 marks.]*
2 a)   They have a biconcave disc shape to give a large surface area for absorbing and releasing oxygen *[1 mark]*. They don't have a nucleus, which allows more room to carry oxygen *[1 mark]*. They are small and very flexible which allows them to pass easily through the capillaries *[1 mark]*.

b) Haemoglobin carries oxygen to body tissues *[1 mark]*. If there is less haemoglobin in the red blood cells, then the blood will be less able to carry oxygen *[1 mark]*. This means that the body tissues will receive less oxygen, reducing the amount of aerobic respiration that can take place *[1 mark]*. This means that less energy is transferred by respiration, causing tiredness *[1 mark]*.

Page 86-87 — The Nervous System

1 receptors *[1 mark]*, sensory *[1 mark]*, motor *[1 mark]*, effectors *[1 mark]*

2 Reflex reactions are rapid and involuntary *[1 mark]*

3 a) i) Y — sensory neurone *[1 mark]*
Z — relay neurone *[1 mark]*
ii) synapse *[1 mark]*
b) the stimulus — flame/heat *[1 mark]*
the effector — muscle (in arm) *[1 mark]*
c) The conscious brain isn't involved in a reflex arc *[1 mark]*.

4 a) i)

[1 mark]
ii) Part X is the fatty/myelin sheath *[1 mark]*. It speeds up the electrical/nervous impulse along the neurone *[1 mark]*.
b) The motor neurones don't work properly, so impulses don't get passed on from the CNS *[1 mark]* to the muscles involved in swallowing *[1 mark]*.

5 By preventing the release of transmitter chemicals, opioids prevent information being transmitted across synapses *[1 mark]* between sensory neurones and (relay) neurones in the spinal cord *[1 mark]*. This means the information about the stimulus doesn't reach the brain, so no pain is felt *[1 mark]*.

Page 88 — The Brain

1 a) A *[1 mark]*
b) conscious movement *[1 mark]*
c) B *[1 mark]*
d) Electrically stimulating different parts of the brain *[1 mark]*. Studying patients with brain damage *[1 mark]*.

2 a) the cerebral cortex *[1 mark]*
b) Any two from: e.g. the tumour may be hard to access. / Surgery to remove the tumour may leave the surrounding parts of Sara's brain damaged. / Further damage to her brain might not be easily repaired. *[2 marks — 1 mark for each correct answer.]*

Page 89 — Hormones and Negative Feedback

1 a) Hormones are released from the endocrine glands directly into the blood *[1 mark]*. The blood then carries them to other parts of the body *[1 mark]*. The hormones then bind to receptors on particular effectors and a response is triggered *[1 mark]*.
b) E.g. a hormonal response is slower than a nervous response *[1 mark]*. The effects of a hormonal response are longer lasting than the effects of a nervous response *[1 mark]*.
c) When the level of a hormone in the blood is above or below the normal level, a response is triggered by negative feedback to bring the level back to normal again *[1 mark]*.

2 a) E.g. it regulates metabolic rate *[1 mark]*.
b) When the level of thyroxine in the blood is higher than normal, the secretion of TSH from the pituitary gland is inhibited *[1 mark]*. This means that the thyroid gland is not stimulated to produce thyroxine *[1 mark]*, and so the blood thyroxine level falls *[1 mark]*.
c) E.g. a stressful situation *[1 mark]*. Adrenaline prepares the body for 'fight or flight' *[1 mark]* by activating processes that increase the supply of oxygen and glucose to cells, e.g. it raises heart rate *[1 mark]*.

Page 90 — Hormones in Reproduction

1 a) A *[1 mark]*
Oestrogen and progesterone are involved in the growth and maintenance of the uterus lining, so menstruation (the breakdown of the uterus lining) occurs during time period A when the levels of these two hormones are low.
b) oestrogen *[1 mark]*, progesterone *[1 mark]*
c) i) It causes an egg to mature in one of the ovaries *[1 mark]* and stimulates the ovaries to produce hormones/oestrogen *[1 mark]*.
ii) After ovulation, the remains of the follicle develop into a corpus luteum *[1 mark]*, which secretes progesterone *[1 mark]*. Progesterone inhibits the release of FSH *[1 mark]* along with oestrogen *[1 mark]*.

Page 91 — Hormones for Fertility and Contraception

1 a) Having low FSH levels can mean that eggs don't mature *[1 mark]*, so ovulation doesn't take place *[1 mark]*.
b) LH/luteinising hormone *[1 mark]*

2 a) oestrogen *[1 mark]*
b) i) Progesterone in the pill inhibits the production of FSH and LH *[1 mark]*, which stimulate egg maturation and ovulation *[1 mark]*.
ii) E.g. it stimulates the production of thick cervical mucus, making it less likely that any sperm will get through and reach an egg *[1 mark]*. / It thins the lining of the uterus, which reduces the chance of a fertilised egg implanting *[1 mark]*.
c) E.g. she doesn't need to remember to take a pill (at the same time) every day *[1 mark]*.

Page 92 — More on Contraception

Warm-up
Circled: male condom, female condom, sterilisation, diaphragm, intrauterine devices, 'natural' methods

1 a) female condom/diaphragm *[1 mark]*
b) They stop the egg and sperm meeting *[1 mark]*.
c) E.g. hormonal methods are generally more effective at preventing pregnancy than barrier methods when used correctly *[1 mark]*. Hormonal methods mean the couple don't have to think about contraception each time they have intercourse, unlike with barrier methods *[1 mark]*.
d) E.g. some barrier methods (such as condoms) can also help to prevent the transmission of STIs *[1 mark]*. It is less likely that there will be unpleasant side effects as a result of using barrier methods than using hormonal methods *[1 mark]*.

Page 93 — Homeostasis

1 allowing large fluctuations in internal conditions *[1 mark]*

2 a) 15 minutes *[1 mark]*
Make sure you include the units when reading data off a graph like this.
b) 30 – 20 = 10 min
35.0 – 34.5 = 0.5 °C
0.5 ÷ 10 = **0.05 °C/min** *[2 marks for correct answer, otherwise 1 mark for 0.5 ÷ 10.]*

Chapter B5

c) It contains receptors that are sensitive to the blood temperature in the brain *[1 mark]*. It also receives impulses from receptors in the skin that provide information about the external temperature *[1 mark]*.

d) Any two from: e.g. erector muscles relax/hairs lie flat. / Lots of sweat is produced. / Blood vessels close to the surface of the skin dilate (widen)/vasodilation occurs *[2 marks — 1 mark for each correct answer]*.

Page 94 — More on Homeostasis
Warm-up

Clockwise from top left: body detects temperature is too **high**, effectors respond to **decrease** body temperature, **normal** body temperature, effectors respond to **increase** body temperature, body detects temperature is too **low**.

1 a) i) processing centre/hypothalamus *[1 mark]*
   ii) effector *[1 mark]*
  b) E.g. relight the Bunsen burner *[1 mark]*.
  c) E.g. the student's claim is incorrect because his model only has a single effector (the Bunsen burner) *[1 mark]*. To make his claim correct he would need to add a second effector that works in opposition to the Bunsen burner *[1 mark]*, e.g. an ice cube that would cool the water *[1 mark]*.

Page 95 — Controlling Water Content
1 a) tubule *[1 mark]*
  b) urea *[1 mark]*
  c) E.g. water/salt *[1 mark]*
2 a) There will be a net movement of water out of the cell by osmosis *[1 mark]*. This will cause the cell to shrink *[1 mark]*.
  b) If there was a higher concentration of water molecules in the tissue fluid than in the cell/the tissue fluid was a less concentrated solution than the fluid in the cell *[1 mark]*, there would be a net movement of water into the cell by osmosis *[1 mark]*. If too much water moved into the cell, it could burst *[1 mark]*.
  c) The concentration of water molecules in the tissue fluid will be the same as the concentration inside the cell *[1 mark]*.

Pages 96-97 — More on Controlling Water Content
Warm-up

hypothalamus, pituitary, more, more, water

1 Negative feedback returns the water content to normal *[1 mark]*.
2 a) Percentage of water not reabsorbed = 100 – 99.2 = 0.8%
    So amount of water lost in urine = 0.8% of 180 dm³
    = (180 ÷ 100) × 0.8 = **1.44 dm³/day**
    [3 marks for correct answer, otherwise 1 mark for 100 – 99.2 and 1 mark for 0.8% of 180 dm³.]
    Or: Percentage of water reabsorbed = 99.2% of 180 dm³
    = (180 ÷ 100) × 99.2 = 178.56 dm³/day
    So amount of water lost in urine = 180 – 178.56
    = **1.44 dm³/day**
    [3 marks for correct answer, otherwise 1 mark for 99.2% of 180 dm³ and 1 mark for 180 – 178.56.]
  b) If the body loses more water than is taken in this causes dehydration *[1 mark]*. This triggers the release of more ADH *[1 mark]* meaning that the kidney will reabsorb more water *[1 mark]*. This leads to a small volume of concentrated urine being produced *[1 mark]*.

3 How to grade your answer:
  Level 0: There is no relevant information. *[No marks]*
  Level 1: There is an attempt to explain how the body responds to high water content. The points made are basic and not linked together. *[1 to 2 marks]*
  Level 2: There is some explanation of how the body responds to high water content, including some detail of the hormones and structures involved. Some of the points made are linked together. *[3 to 4 marks]*
  Level 3: There is a full and clear explanation of how the body responds to high water content. All relevant hormones and structures are included in the answer and referred to correctly. The points made are well-linked and the answer has a clear and logical structure. *[5 to 6 marks]*

Here are some points your answer may include:
The brain monitors the water content of the blood. If the brain detects a high water concentration it instructs the pituitary gland to release less ADH (anti-diuretic hormone) into the bloodstream. ADH makes the kidney tubules more permeable so that more water is reabsorbed back into the blood. Releasing less ADH into the bloodstream means that the tubules are less permeable and the kidney reabsorbs less water. This means that more water is lost in the urine and there will be a larger volume of urine produced. This will cause the water content of the blood to decrease. This returns the level of water in the blood to a normal level.

4 If not enough ADH is produced then the kidney tubules will be less permeable *[1 mark]* and not enough water will be reabsorbed from the kidneys into the blood *[1 mark]*. This will mean that the water content of the blood falls *[1 mark]*, so the person will need to drink more water to maintain the water content of the blood *[1 mark]*.

Page 98-99 — Controlling Blood Sugar Level
1 a) i) insulin *[1 mark]*
    ii) glucagon *[1 mark]*
  b) It is stored as glycogen in the liver and in the muscles. / It is stored as lipid (fat) in the tissues *[1 mark]*.
2 a) The pancreas stops producing insulin *[1 mark]*.
  b) E.g. a person's blood glucose level can rise to a level that can kill them *[1 mark]*.
  c) E.g. the person's diet. / How active the person is *[1 mark]*.
  d) A person becomes resistant to insulin/their body cells no longer respond to the insulin *[1 mark]*. / A person doesn't produce enough insulin *[1 mark]*.
  e) Any two from: eating a healthy diet, including replacing simple carbohydrates with complex carbohydrates *[1 mark]* / getting regular exercise *[1 mark]* / losing weight (if necessary) *[1 mark]*.
  f) being overweight / obesity *[1 mark]*
3 a) The blood glucose concentration starts increasing as glucose from the drink is absorbed into the blood *[1 mark]*. The pancreas detects a high blood glucose concentration and secretes insulin *[1 mark]*. Insulin causes the blood glucose concentration to fall back down *[1 mark]*.
  b) glucagon *[1 mark]*
  c) It increases the concentration of glucose in the blood *[1 mark]*.
  d) Glucagon causes glycogen to be converted into glucose and be released into the blood *[1 mark]*.
  e) E.g. after drinking the glucose drink, the blood glucose concentration would carry on increasing/stay high/not start to fall/fall more slowly *[1 mark]*.

Chapter B6

Page 100 — The Eye
Warm-up

1 a) The lens refracts light and focuses it onto the retina *[1 mark]*.
   b) Ciliary muscles *[1 mark]* and suspensory ligaments *[1 mark]*.
2 a) Eye B, because the pupil is wider to let in more light *[1 mark]*.
   b) So that the amount of light entering the eye can be controlled *[1 mark]* so that bright light cannot damage the retina *[1 mark]* and to allow sufficient light to enter the eye in dim conditions *[1 mark]*.

Page 101-102 — Correcting Vision Defects
1 a) Cataracts are cloudy patches on the lens *[1 mark]*. The clouding of the lens stops light from being able to enter the eye normally *[1 mark]*.
   b) By replacing the faulty lens with an artificial one *[1 mark]*.
2 a) short-sightedness *[1 mark]*
   b) The lens refracts light rays so that they diverge before they enter the eye *[1 mark]*. This reduces convergence, allowing the image to be brought into focus on the retina *[1 mark]*.
   c) E.g.

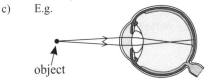

object

   [1 mark for 2 rays of light converging, 1 mark for rays meeting in front of the retina.]
3 a) Light rays entering the eye don't converge enough *[1 mark]* so images aren't brought into focus on the retina/are brought into focus behind the retina *[1 mark]*.
   b) Convex lenses/lenses that are fattest in the centre *[1 mark]* can be used to refract light so that it starts to converge before it enters the eye *[1 mark]*. This increased convergence allows the image to be brought into focus on the retina *[1 mark]*.
4 The cornea is the wrong shape *[1 mark]* which will change the amount by which it refracts/bends light into the eye *[1 mark]* so images will not be focused on the retina *[1 mark]*.

Chapter B6 — Life on Earth — Past, Present and Future

Pages 103-104 — Natural Selection and Evolution
1 a) Most genetic variants have very little or no effect on the phenotype of an organism *[1 mark]*.
   b) It describes how beneficial genetic variants become more common in a population *[1 mark]*.
   c) By mutations in DNA *[1 mark]*.
2 a) E.g. organisms have to compete for resources in order to survive *[1 mark]*, so not all organisms will survive to reproduce and pass their genes on to the next generation *[1 mark]*.
   b) Natural selection means that organisms with the most beneficial genetic variants/alleles *[1 mark]* are more likely to pass on their genes to the next generation *[1 mark]*. Over time this may lead to the most beneficial genetic variants/alleles accumulating in a population and therefore a reduction in the level of genetic variation *[1 mark]*.

3 a) E.g. they could allow the two species of wasp to breed with each other and if they are unable to produce fertile offspring the species are separate *[1 mark]*.
   b) A single population of species A became split into two isolated populations when the islands became separated *[1 mark]*. The environmental conditions on each island were different *[1 mark]* and led to natural selection for different genetic variants/alleles in both populations *[1 mark]*. Over time, the different genetic variants/alleles accumulated in both populations until the two populations were so different they were different species *[1 mark]*.
4 How to grade your answer:
   Level 0: There is no relevant information. *[0 marks]*
   Level 1: There is some information about evolution by natural selection. The points made are basic and not linked together. *[1-2 marks]*
   Level 2: There is some explanation about how evolution by natural selection may lead to a change in the beak size of the finches. Some of the points made are linked together. *[3-4 marks]*
   Level 3: There is a clear and detailed explanation of how evolution by natural selection may lead to a change in the beak size of the finches. The points made are well-linked and the answer has a clear and logical structure. *[5-6 marks]*
   Here are some points your answer may include:
   After the storm, there will be fewer larger seeds available on the island. Birds with larger beaks will be less able to get food. Small seeds will still be available, so birds with smaller beaks will be better adapted to their environment than the birds with larger beaks. This makes birds with smaller beaks more likely to survive and reproduce than birds with larger beaks. In turn, this means that the genetic variants/alleles responsible for small beaks are more likely to be passed on to the next generation than the genetic variants/alleles for larger beaks. The genetic variants/alleles for smaller beaks will become more common in the population over time and, eventually, all the finches in the population will have smaller beaks.

Page 105 — Evidence for Evolution
1 a) The remains of an insect which died recently *[1 mark]*.
   b) Fossil B, Fossil A, Human foot *[1 mark]*
You know that the fossils are form the ancestors of humans, so the human foot must be the most recent. Fossil A more closely resembles the human foot than fossil B, so it must be the next most recent.
2 a) The fast reproduction rate means the scientists can study evolution as it is happening *[1 mark]*.
   b) By mutations in the bacterial DNA *[1 mark]*.
   c) The findings suggest that bacterial cells with the ability to use citrate as food source are more likely to survive once the glucose supply has run out *[1 mark]*. These bacterial cells are therefore more likely to reproduce and pass on their genes to the next generation *[1 mark]*, meaning that the ability to use citrate has become more common in the population *[1 mark]*.

Page 106 — Selective Breeding
Warm-up
Producing bacteria with the human gene for insulin. Creating hens that lay eggs containing human proteins. Creating a crop plant that secretes scorpion venom.
Selective breeding is used to create different varieties of the same species. It can't be used to introduce genetic material from another organism, such as a gene from a human into a bacterium — for this you would need to use genetic engineering techniques.

Chapter B6

1 Darwin noticed that selective breeding produced new varieties of organisms which were sometimes very different to their wild ancestors *[1 mark]*. This led him to think that natural processes selected individuals with traits which made them more likely to survive in an environment *[1 mark]*, meaning that these traits became more common and the species evolved *[1 mark]*.

2 a) Select only those hens with a high egg production for further breeding with males *[1 mark]*. Select the offspring with the highest egg production and breed them with males *[1 mark]*. Continue to breed the most desirable offspring over several generations, so that the egg production gets higher and higher *[1 mark]*.

b) The selective breeding of the cows has reduced the gene pool for his herd *[1 mark]*. A smaller gene pool means that it's more likely that individuals will inherit harmful genetic defects, such as Weaver Syndrome *[1 mark]*.

Page 107 — Darwin and Wallace

1 Natural selection *[1 mark]*

2 a) Any two from: e.g. now that we understand evolutionary relationships, we can classify organisms based on their evolutionary ancestry. / Now that we understand how antibiotic-resistant bacteria evolve, we know that we have to keep developing new antibiotics. / Our understanding of the importance of genetic variation and how it helps populations adapt to changing environments has influenced conservation projects to protect species. *[2 marks — 1 mark for each correct answer.]*

b) Any two from: e.g. they misunderstand the theory. / They are not aware of the evidence for the theory. / They don't believe in it (due to religious beliefs). *[2 marks — 1 mark for each correct answer.]*

3 Isolated populations of the same species would be exposed to different environmental conditions *[1 mark]*. Organisms with characteristics that made them more well-suited to their environment would be more likely to survive and pass on their characteristics to the next generation *[1 mark]*. Over time this would lead to many members of the population having the advantageous characteristics, meaning there would be observable differences between the separated populations *[1 mark]*.

Page 108 — Asexual and Sexual Reproduction

Warm-Up
true, true, false

1 a) Asexual reproduction *[1 mark]*, because there is only one parent *[1 mark]*.

b) It allows lots of offspring to be produced very quickly *[1 mark]*. / The female can reproduce when conditions are favourable without having to wait for a mate *[1 mark]*.

2 a) The sexually reproducing patch because it takes time for the gametes of two parent plants to meet and fuse together/ the reproductive cycle is much slower than for asexual reproduction *[1 mark]*.

b) The patch that reproduces sexually, because it will have more genetic variation *[1 mark]* and therefore it will be more likely that some plants in the patch will have characteristics that enable them to survive the environmental change *[1 mark]*.

Page 109 — Classification

1 a) The grouping of living organisms *[1 mark]* based on similarities and differences between them *[1 mark]*.

b) i) B *[1 mark]*
   ii) G and H *[1 mark]*

2 a) Organism F *[1 mark]* as its DNA has the highest percentage similarity (96%) to human DNA of the organisms in the table *[1 mark]*.

b) Scientists can find the number of genetic variants between two species *[1 mark]* and use an estimate for the frequency at which mutations happen in each species *[1 mark]* to estimate how long ago speciation occurred *[1 mark]*.

Pages 110-111 — Biodiversity

Warm-up
greater, more, damage, decrease

1 a) The rate at which resources are used is not greater than the rate at which they can be replaced *[1 mark]*.

b) living organisms *[1 mark]*, genes and alleles *[1 mark]*

2 a) Human activities are having such a rapid effect that there is not enough time for populations to adapt to the changes *[1 mark]*.

b) E.g. the loss of one species can impact on food chains *[1 mark]*, and may lead to the loss of other species *[1 mark]*.

3 a) E.g. increasing industrialisation is leading to an increased use of raw materials *[1 mark]*. This has led to increased habitat destruction in the extraction of raw materials *[1 mark]*. Increasing industrialisation has also led to the increased production of waste from industrial processes *[1 mark]*. This can result in increased pollution of ecosystems *[1 mark]*.

b) E.g. large companies may sell the 'best' variety of a particular natural resource (such as seeds), resulting in it being used across the world *[1 mark]*, reducing the number of varieties used globally, and reducing global biodiversity *[1 mark]*.

4 How to grade your answer:
Level 0: There is no relevant information. *[0 marks]*
Level 1: There is some discussion of how humans can help to protect biodiversity on several different levels. The points made are basic and not linked together. *[1-2 marks]*
Level 2: There is some discussion of how humans can help to protect biodiversity on a species, habitat and global level. Some of the points made are linked together. *[3-4 marks]*
Level 3: There is a clear and detailed discussion of how humans can help to protect biodiversity on a species, habitat and global level. The points made are well-linked and the answer has a clear and logical structure. *[5-6 marks]*

Here are some points your answer may include:
Humans can protect individual species by banning the hunting of the species, or by keeping individuals of the species in safe areas away from hunting or habitat destruction. Safe areas for animals include zoos and for plants they include botanical gardens and seed banks. Humans can protect habitats and ecosystems by creating protected areas such as national parks and nature reserves in which development of land is restricted. They can also create protected areas in the sea to protect marine ecosystems from human activities such as fishing. Humans could help to protect biodiversity on a global scale by reducing the amount of greenhouse gases released by human activities. This would help to reduce global warming. Global warming may lead to the extinction of species, so preventing it from happening would help to protect global biodiversity.

Page 112 — Biodiversity and the Distribution of Organisms

1 a) They are positively correlated *[1 mark]*.
b) 900 mm/year *[1 mark]*

Answers

Mixed Questions

2 a) The results show that the total number of different species in each group decreased *[1 mark]*, which suggests biodiversity in the area has decreased *[1 mark]*.

b) Seasonal variations in the environment may affect the distribution of species *[1 mark]*, so the data must be compared from the same season so that any changes are more likely to be due to the flooding *[1 mark]*.

Page 113 — Maintaining Biodiversity

1 a) If one species goes extinct then the food chain that it is a part of will be disrupted *[1 mark]*. Protecting one species, will help to protect the species that feed on it *[1 mark]*. / Efforts to protect one species may involve the protection of the habitat of that species *[1 mark]*, in which case, other species within that habitat will also be protected *[1 mark]*.

b) E.g. the costs involved in conserving the species may outweigh the potential benefit *[1 mark]*.

2 a) E.g. regions of high biodiversity may have plants which contain undiscovered medicines which could be used by humans *[1 mark]*. / Protecting regions of high biodiversity may help to protect species which are used by humans for industrial materials and fuels *[1 mark]*. / Protecting regions of high biodiversity may help to protect the human food supply *[1 mark]*.

b) E.g. protected areas prevent people from being able to use the land for human activities such as building/farming *[1 mark]* or for using/selling the natural resources it has *[1 mark]*. Some people think this is morally wrong in developing countries because these activities could help to boost their economy *[1 mark]*.

c) E.g. it may be difficult to get two or more countries to work together to establish parks like La Amistad International Park *[1 mark]*, because they may not be willing to sign up to an agreement not to develop the land *[1 mark]*.

Pages 114-115 — Human Food Security

1 a) Everyone having access to enough food which is safe to eat *[1 mark]*.

b) The appearance of a new pathogen of food crops *[1 mark]*.

2 a) More food is needed globally each year to ensure food security *[1 mark]* because the human population is rising *[1 mark]*.

b) E.g. increased pollution *[1 mark]*, may affect our ability to grow crops *[1 mark]*. / An increased global temperature *[1 mark]* could affect the growth patterns of crops resulting in a reduction in yield *[1 mark]*.

c) E.g. wealthier populations may eat more meat, which could negatively impact global food security *[1 mark]*. This is because animals being reared for meat graze on land that could be used to grow crops for humans *[1 mark]*, and they also are fed crops that could be given directly to humans *[1 mark]*.

3 a) E.g. livestock may be vaccinated against diseases caused by pathogens *[1 mark]*. Antibiotics can be given to livestock to protect them against bacterial pathogens *[1 mark]*.

b) E.g. use of genetically engineered crops that are resistant to pests *[1 mark]*.

4 a) Farm A has a higher milk yield than farm B *[1 mark]*, because its cows have access to enough nutrients and energy for their health and growth *[1 mark]*.

b) Farm C would have high input costs due to the cost of heating and machinery *[1 mark]*, which may be too expensive for smaller farms to afford *[1 mark]*.

Mixed Questions

Pages 116-124 — Mixed Questions

1 a) i) mitochondria *[1 mark]*
   ii) carbon dioxide *[1 mark]*, water *[1 mark]*
   b) i) plasma *[1 mark]*
   ii) Glucagon is released into the blood *[1 mark]*, which converts glycogen back into glucose *[1 mark]*.

2 a) producer *[1 mark]*
   b)
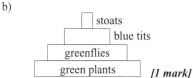
   Don't forget, the producer always goes on the bottom of a pyramid of biomass, then the next trophic level goes on top of that and so on.
   c) Biotic: e.g. an increase in greenfly numbers / the presence of a new pathogen *[1 mark]*.
   Abiotic: e.g. a change in light intensity / toxic chemicals / moisture level / temperature / soil pH *[1 mark]*.
   Remember, biotic factors are 'living' factors that affect an environment, and abiotic factors are 'non-living' factors.

3 a) i) a protein *[1 mark]*
   ii) kidney *[1 mark]*
   b) Enzymes speed up chemical reactions in living organisms. *[1 mark]*
   c) i) 40 °C *[1 mark]*
   ii) The enzyme will not work *[1 mark]* because the high temperature will change the shape of its active site/denature the enzyme *[1 mark]* and the substrate will no longer fit *[1 mark]*.

4 a) RR *[1 mark]*
   b) round seed shape *[1 mark]*
   c)

	Ⓡ	Ⓡ
ⓡ	Rr	Rr
ⓡ	Rr	Rr

[1 mark]
   The parents' genotypes were RR and rr *[1 mark]*.

5 a) Effectors have receptors that are specific to certain hormones *[1 mark]*. Only the right hormones will bind to these receptors and have an effect *[1 mark]*.
   b) Because hormones are transported round the body in the blood, which is relatively slow *[1 mark]* and the nervous response involves electrical impulses, which are very fast *[1 mark]*.
   c) i) blood sugar/glucose level *[1 mark]*
   ii) diabetes *[1 mark]*
   d) i) LH *[1 mark]*
   ii) oestrogen *[1 mark]*
   e) They are inhibited by the hormones represented by lines C and D/oestrogen and progesterone *[1 mark]*.

6 a) i) A non-communicable disease because it is not transmitted between individuals/is not caused by a pathogen *[1 mark]*.
   Remember, communicable diseases are caused by pathogens and can be spread between individuals. Vitamin A deficiency is caused by deficiencies in the diet, so it's non-communicable.
   ii) E.g. it could make a person more susceptible to infection/communicable disease *[1 mark]* as the body would be less able to fight off infection by pathogens *[1 mark]*.
   b) It will contain genes not found in normal rice / DNA from a bacterium and a maize plant *[1 mark]*.

Answers

Mixed Questions

c) E.g. the genes to be used from the maize plant and the soil bacterium were isolated and replicated/copied *[1 mark]*. The copies were then inserted into vectors *[1 mark]*. The vectors were then inserted into the cells of (embryonic) rice plants *[1 mark]* and plants that had taken up the vectors containing the desired genes were selected to produce Golden Rice *[1 mark]*.

7 a) i) There is less variation (in tomato size) in Generation X than in Generation A *[1 mark]*. This is because selective breeding has led to a smaller gene pool/a smaller variety of alleles in Generation X than in Generation A *[1 mark]*.

   ii) 17.1 – 12.7 = 4.4 cm
   (4.4 ÷ 12.7) × 100 = **34.6%**
   [2 marks for correct answer, otherwise 1 mark for correct working.]

To calculate percentage change, you first need to work out the difference between the two figures. You then need calculate what percentage that difference is of the first figure.

b) i) The tomato plants absorb nitrate ions via active transport *[1 mark]* through the partially permeable membranes of their root hair cells *[1 mark]*.

   ii) Eutrophication involves increased algal growth *[1 mark]*, which blocks out light for plants growing in the water, causing them to die *[1 mark]*. Microorganisms feeding on the dead plants use up oxygen in the water *[1 mark]*, which results in the death of other organisms, such as fish *[1 mark]*.

8 a) i) Tube 1 *[1 mark]*

   ii) Tube 1 shows that in the dark, the algae are producing more carbon dioxide than they take in *[1 mark]*. The concentration of carbon dioxide is high because the cells are respiring, but not photosynthesising (as there's no light for photosynthesis to take place) *[1 mark]*. Tube 2 shows that in the light, the algae are taking up more carbon dioxide than they produce *[1 mark]*. The concentration of carbon dioxide has reduced because the cells are photosynthesising faster than they are respiring *[1 mark]*.

Plant cells respire all the time but they can only photosynthesise when it's light.

   iii) Any two from: e.g. the temperature of the boiling tubes / the volume of hydrogencarbonate indicator / the concentration of hydrogencarbonate indicator / the number of beads in each tube / the concentration of algal cells in each bead *[2 marks — 1 mark for each correct answer]*.

b) i) Light intensity *[1 mark]* because the rate of photosynthesis is increasing as the light intensity increases *[1 mark]*.

   ii) carbon dioxide concentration *[1 mark]*

9 a) mitosis *[1 mark]*

b) There are fewer red blood cells to carry oxygen to all the cells in the body *[1 mark]*. This means that the cells aren't receiving enough oxygen for respiration/transferring energy from glucose *[1 mark]*.

c) i) Monoclonal antibodies that are complementary to the malaria antigen *[1 mark]* and labelled with dye *[1 mark]*.

   ii) E.g. the flushing agent is used to help the blood sample flow from one end of the stick to the other through the paper strip *[1 mark]*.

   iii) A coloured line has appeared in area B because malaria antigens are present in the blood sample *[1 mark]*. Monoclonal antibodies complementary to the malaria antigen are stuck to the strip in area B *[1 mark]*. Malaria antigens bound to the dye-labelled antibodies have flowed along the strip from area A to area B *[1 mark]* where they have bound to antibodies that are stuck to the strip *[1 mark]*. Because the antibodies containing dye have bound to the strip in area B they are visible there as a coloured line *[1 mark]*.

d) Malaria protists of different species may have different antigens on their surfaces *[1 mark]* so the memory cells created after vaccination against *Plasmodium falciparum* won't recognise them/produce antibodies against them *[1 mark]*.

ISBN 978 1 78294 510 9

9 781782 945109

B2QA41   £2.00
               (Retail Price)

www.cgpbooks.co.uk

GCSE Biology

For OCR 21st Century (Grade 9-1)

Exam Practice Answer Book

For the new course starting September 2016

Contents

Published by CGP

ISBN: 978 1 78294 510 9

www.cgpbooks.co.uk
Printed by Elanders Ltd, Newcastle upon Tyne.
Clipart from Corel®
Text, design, layout and original illustrations © Coordination Group Publications Ltd. (CGP) 2016

Chapter B1

Chapter B1 — You and Your Genes

Page 1 — Cells and Genetic Material

1 a)   bacterium *[1 mark]*
  b) i)   X – chromosome/DNA/genetic material *[1 mark]*
         Y – cell membrane *[1 mark]*
         Z – plasmid *[1 mark]*
     ii) It contains genetic material *[1 mark]*.
  c)   It contains instructions that control the activity of the cell *[1 mark]*.
  d) i)   10 times larger / 1 order of magnitude larger *[1 mark]*
     ii) Any two from: e.g. eukaryotic cells have a nucleus, prokaryotic cells do not. / DNA is found inside the nucleus of eukaryotic cells, but is not enclosed in prokaryotic cells. / Prokaryotic cells may contain plasmids, eukaryotic cells do not. / Eukaryotic cells have mitochondria, prokaryotic cells do not. *[2 marks — 1 mark for each correct answer.]*

Page 2 — Cells and Microscopes

1 a) i)   So that light can pass through the specimen *[1 mark]*.
     ii) The student used iodine solution to stain the specimen *[1 mark]* so that she could see the onion cells more clearly *[1 mark]*.
  b) i)   × 4 *[1 mark]*
Remember, you should always start with the lowest-powered objective lens — this makes it easier to get your specimen into view.
     ii) They bring the sample into focus by moving the stage up and down *[1 mark]*.

     iii) She should select the × 40 or × 100 objective lens *[1 mark]* and use the adjustment knobs to bring the sample back into focus *[1 mark]*.
  c)   Any two from: e.g. she should use a sharp pencil. / She should not colour or shade her drawing. / She should label her drawing with straight, uncrossing lines. / She should include the magnification used and a scale. / Her drawing should take up at least half of the space available. / She should keep the parts in proportion. *[2 marks — 1 for each correct answer.]*

Page 3-4 — Genomes and Characteristics

Warm-up
polymer — a long chain of repeating molecules
nucleotide — the repeating unit that makes up DNA
double helix — the spiral shape of a DNA molecule
allele — a version of a gene
1 a)   DNA is located in the nucleus of animal and plant cells *[1 mark]*.
  b)   The structures that contain DNA *[1 mark]*.
  c)   Genes code for particular sequences of amino acids *[1 mark]*, which are put together to make specific proteins *[1 mark]*.
  d)   The entire set of genetic material in an organism *[1 mark]*.
2 a) i)   An organism's genotype is the combination of alleles an organism has for each gene *[1 mark]*. An organism's phenotype is the characteristics that an organism displays *[1 mark]*.

Answers